JOHANN SEBASTIAN

(1685-1750)
EIGHTEEN LITTLE PRELUDES
Edited by Keith Snell

According to Bach's sons, Wilhelm Friedemann and Philipp Emanuel, it was very important to Bach that his students develop a "clear, clean touch of all the fingers of both hands." To accomplish this, Bach assigned many finger exercises for his students to practice. In addition, Bach would compose short pieces developed from the finger exercises he assigned. The *Eighteen Little Preludes* are pieces of this origin. Many times Bach wrote a prelude during a student's lesson, and later refined it into a beautiful and complete work of art.

CONTENTS

For supplementary study, a recording is available on compact disc of the Eighteen Little Preludes, *performed by pianist Diane Hidy (GP383CD). Ms.Hidy's interpretations follow this edition closely as a practical example for students.*

ISBN 0-8497-6198-0

2

THE BAROQUE PERIOD

The word *baroque* was originally used to describe a style of art and architecture of highly decorative and extravagant design in the 17th and 18th centuries. It is not until the 20th century that the term is used to describe the style of music from approximately 1600 to 1750. J. S. Bach is regarded as the greatest composer of the Baroque period.

JOHANN SEBASTIAN BACH (1685-1750)

Johann Sebastian Bach was born in Eisenach—a small town in central Germany. He came from a very musical family. For almost 200 years before his birth, many of his relatives were well known musicians in Germany. Bach received his first music lessons from his father who taught him to play the violin.

Bach was only 10 years old when his parents died. He then went to live with his older brother, Johann Christoph, who taught him to play keyboard instruments. In addition to his music lessons, he attended the local school where he studied Latin, Greek, theology, and arithmetic.

In 1700 when Bach was 15 years old, he went to live at the church of St. Michael in Lüneburg where he was a choir boy and student. After his voice changed, he continued serving in various musical jobs which began his career as a professional musician.

At the age of 19, he took a job in Weimar as string player and organist. A few months later he found a better position as organist in Arnstadt. He moved again to Mühlhausen where he stayed one year. During this year Bach married his cousin, Maria Barbara Bach. During their marriage they had seven children, but only four lived.

After the year at Mühlhausen, Bach returned to Weimar where he spent nine years employed as composer and organist at the court of Duke Wilhelm Ernst. Disappointed at not being promoted to Music Director, Bach moved on to the court of Prince Leopold of Anhalt in the city of Cöthen. Here Bach became Music Director, in charge of the Prince's singers and the court orchestra.

In 1720 Maria Barbara died. One year later he married his second wife, Anna Magdalena, who was only 20 years old. They had 13 children. Out of the 20 children from Bach's two marriages, 10 died in infancy or at childbirth. From the surviving 10, four of his sons—Carl Philipp Emanuel, Johann Christoph, Johann Christian and Wilhelm Friedemann—became composers.

When he was 38, Bach moved to Leipzig where he became cantor (music teacher) at the St. Thomas School. He remained there until his death 27 years later. During these years Bach was very busy teaching, conducting, performing, and writing music.

In 1750, the last year of his life, Bach's eyesight began to deteriorate. By summer, his health failed and he died on July 28. He was buried in St. John's cemetery. Anna Magdalena lived ten more years, but died in poverty in 1760.

Bach was a prolific composer. His complete works fill 46 large volumes containing choral music, concertos, orchestra and chamber works, and organ and clavier (keyboard) music.

GP383

TABLE OF ORNAMENTS

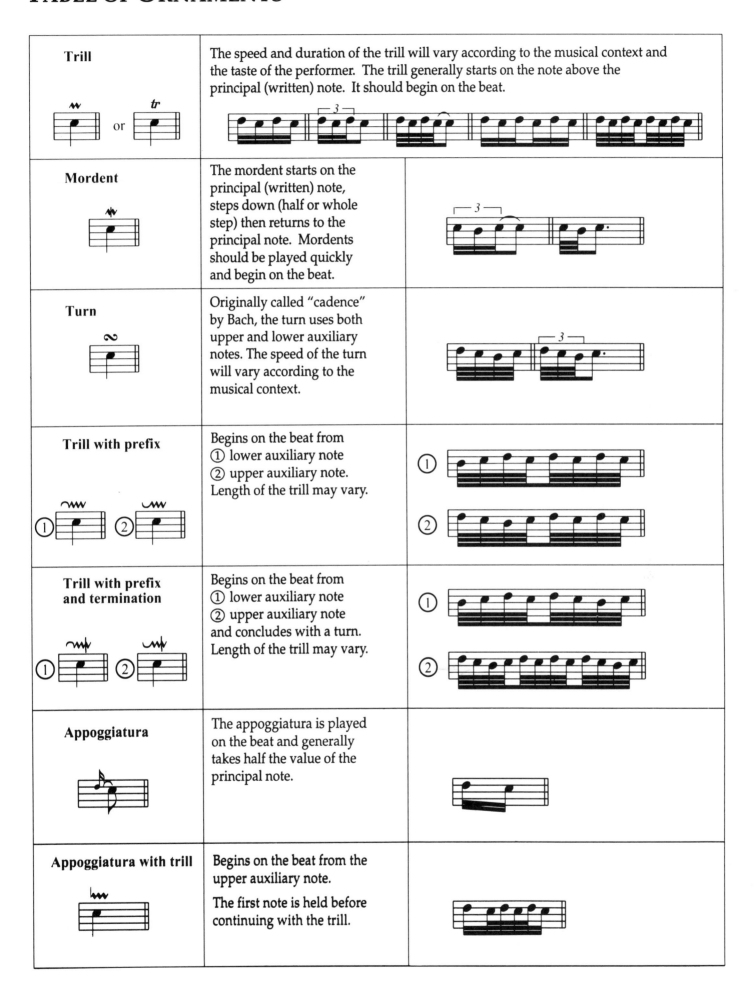

Trill	The speed and duration of the trill will vary according to the musical context and the taste of the performer. The trill generally starts on the note above the principal (written) note. It should begin on the beat.
Mordent	The mordent starts on the principal (written) note, steps down (half or whole step) then returns to the principal note. Mordents should be played quickly and begin on the beat.
Turn	Originally called "cadence" by Bach, the turn uses both upper and lower auxiliary notes. The speed of the turn will vary according to the musical context.
Trill with prefix	Begins on the beat from ① lower auxiliary note ② upper auxiliary note. Length of the trill may vary.
Trill with prefix and termination	Begins on the beat from ① lower auxiliary note ② upper auxiliary note and concludes with a turn. Length of the trill may vary.
Appoggiatura	The appoggiatura is played on the beat and generally takes half the value of the principal note.
Appoggiatura with trill	Begins on the beat from the upper auxiliary note. The first note is held before continuing with the trill.

1. PRELUDE IN C MAJOR

BWV 924

Moderato (60 – 72 = ♩)

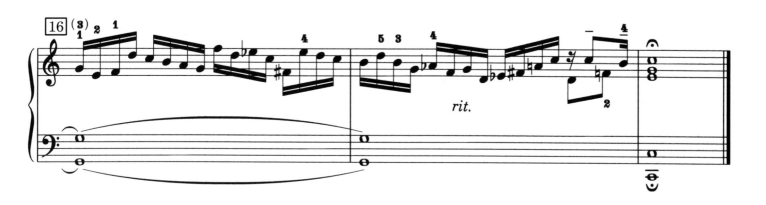

2. PRELUDE IN D MINOR

BWV 926

3. PRELUDE IN F MAJOR

BWV 927

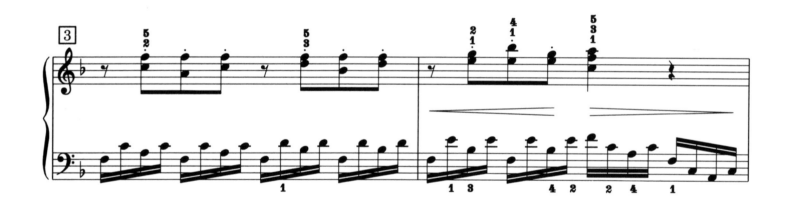

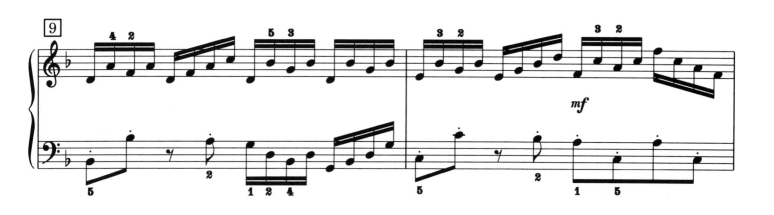

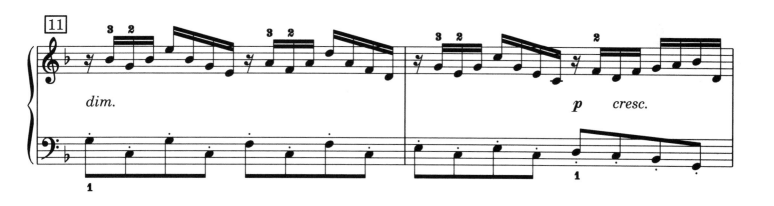

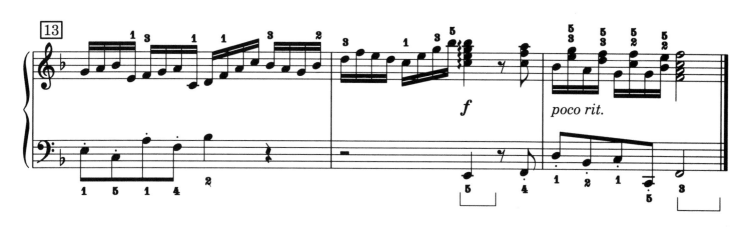

4. PRELUDE IN G MINOR

BWV 930

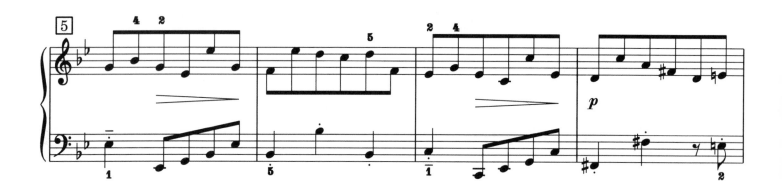

5. PRELUDE IN F MAJOR

BWV 928

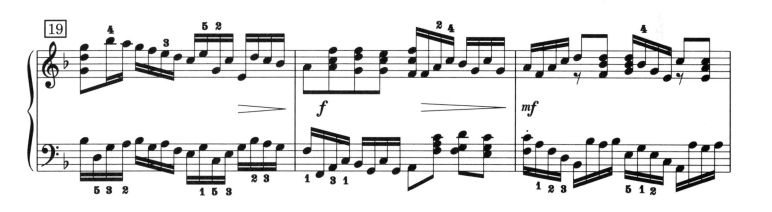

6. PRELUDE IN D MAJOR

BWV 925

7. PRELUDE IN C MAJOR

BWV 933

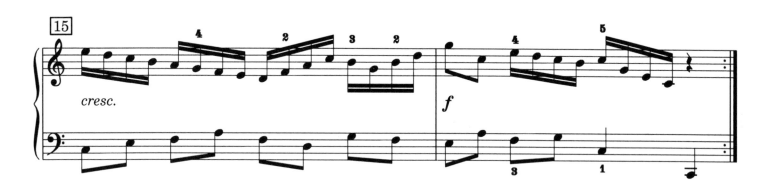

8. PRELUDE IN C MINOR

BWV 934

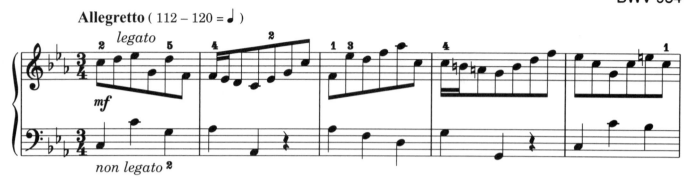

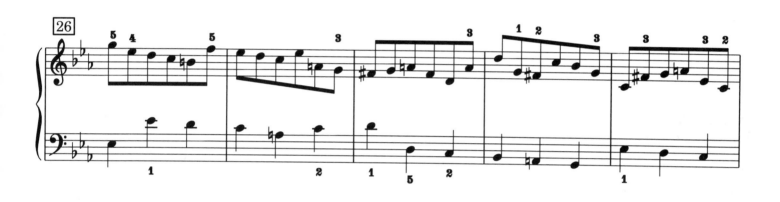

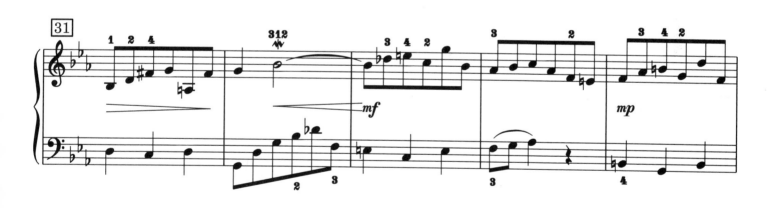

9. PRELUDE IN D MINOR

BWV 935

10. PRELUDE IN D MAJOR

BWV 936

11. PRELUDE IN E MAJOR

BWV 937

12. PRELUDE IN E MINOR

BWV 938

13. PRELUDE IN C MAJOR

BWV 939

14. PRELUDE IN D MINOR

BWV 940

15. PRELUDE IN E MINOR

BWV 941

16. PRELUDE IN A MINOR

BWV 942

17. PRELUDE IN C MAJOR

BWV 943

Allegro moderato (116 – 126 = ♩)

18. PRELUDE IN C MINOR

BWV 999